# Nature STEAM Activities

## REBECCA FELIX

Lerner Publications ◆ Minneapolis

Official Licensed Product
Lerner Publications Company
An imprint of Lerner Publishing Group, Inc.
241 First Avenue North
Minneapolis, MN 55401 USA

For reading levels and more information, look up this title at www.lernerbooks.com.

Main body text set in Syntax LT Std
Typeface provided by Adobe


**Library of Congress Cataloging-in-Publication Data**

Names: Felix, Rebecca, 1984- author. | Crayola (Firm)
Title: Crayola ® nature STEAM activities / Rebecca Felix.
Other titles: Nature STEAM activities
Description: Minneapolis, MN : Lerner Publications Company, an imprint of Lerner Publishing Group, Inc., 2021. | Series: Crayola ® makers | Includes bibliographical references and index. | Audience: Ages 8–11. | Audience: Grades 2–3. | Summary: "These projects and experiments show readers elements of STEAM they can see in nature every day. Build a sundial and a wind vane, and collect leaves, grass, and bugs for observation and exploration"— Provided by publisher.
Identifiers: LCCN 2020034229 (print) | LCCN 2020034230 (ebook) | ISBN 9781728403175 (library binding) | ISBN 9781728417851 (ebook)
Subjects: LCSH: Nature craft—Juvenile literature. | Handicraft for children—Juvenile literature. | Nature observation—Juvenile literature.
Classification: LCC TT157 .F433 2021  (print) | LCC TT157  (ebook) | DDC 745.5083—dc23

LC record available at https://lccn.loc.gov/2020034229
LC ebook record available at https://lccn.loc.gov/2020034230


Manufactured in the United States of America
1-48288-48832-11/11/2020

# TABLE OF CONTENTS

# STEAM Means...

STEAM holds many amazing things in just five letters! Each letter stands for a different discipline. These are science, technology, engineering, arts, and math.

STEAM is all around you, wherever you go! Look outside. Many sciences involve the study of nature. Math sequences and shapes are seen in all sorts of natural things, including flowers, leaves, and animal markings. Engineers consider nature, science, math, and technology when they construct buildings, roads, and vehicles. Art is found in these things too! People use art when designing buildings, signs, and more. And nature inspires people to paint, sculpt, and create amazing artworks.

# Nature & STEAM

Explore STEAM in nature! Make sequences with leaves, construct insect habitats, experiment with art tools made from flowers or moss, and more.

# STEAM Safety

Some projects require the use of heat, sharp tools, or substances that can be unsafe if misused. Follow these rules to explore STEAM safely:

- Ask an adult for permission and help before using heat or sharp tools.

- Do not touch your eyes, nose, or mouth during a STEAM project.

- Wash your hands after using glues, dyes, and paints.

- Read and follow all instructions that come with any product you use.

# Sky-High Stone Sculptures

## Materials:

gathered stones, gathered twigs, paint, paintbrushes, school glue, rubber bands, chenille stems

Stack, connect, and bind stones together to engineer towering works of art!

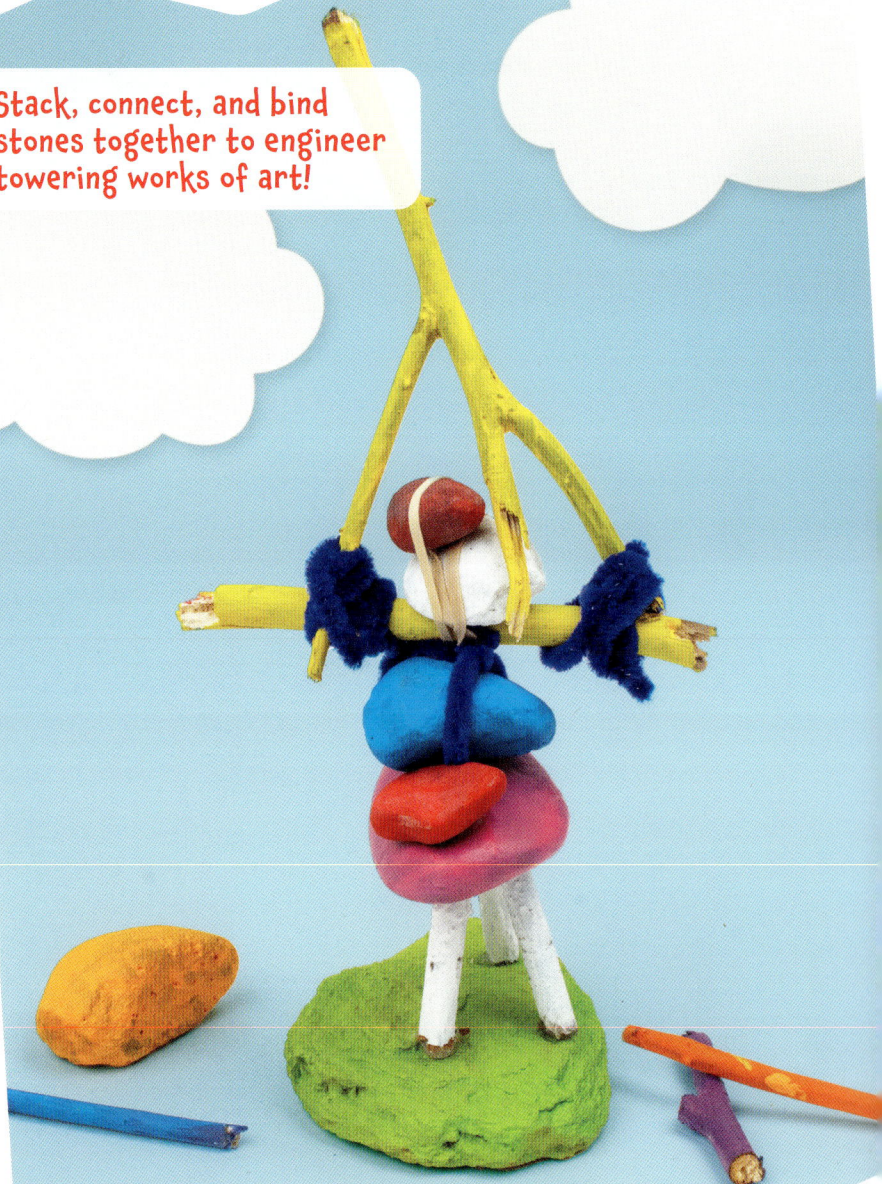

1 Get permission from an adult to explore outdoors. This could be in your yard, a park, or any natural area. Gather some stones and twigs.

2 Paint the objects you gathered. Let the paint dry.

3 Lay out all your materials. Consider each object's properties to decide how to use it in your sculpture. Examples:

- A heavy rock could make a great base.
- Rubber bands and chenille stems are good connectors.
- Twigs can give the sculpture height.

4 Use glue, rubber bands, and chenille stems to connect the rocks and twigs. See how high you can build your sculpture.

5 If your sculpture tips over or falls apart, think about why. Experiment and get creative! What happens if you make the base wider? What if you use more twigs to reinforce it? Is more glue needed to hold the items together?

6 After your first sculpture is done, use any leftover materials to make more. Challenge yourself to engineer structures that are even taller!

# Pattern Gallery

Discover and photograph patterns in nature, then create artworks inspired by their designs.

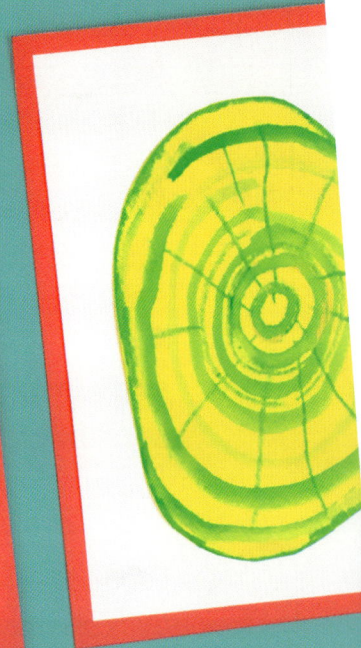

## Materials:

digital camera, smartphone, or tablet; printer; scissors; paint; paintbrushes; markers; colored pencils; crayons; school glue; construction paper

1  Get permission from an adult to explore outdoors. This might be along the sidewalk, at a playground, or in your yard. Search for natural patterns. These may be on a leaf or tree bark. You may spot patterns on flower petals or in the markings of a caterpillar. Look closely!

2  Take photos of the patterns you find. Take several photos to best show off each pattern. Stand back or move in close. Zoom in and switch angles.

3  Review your photos. Choose three of your favorite patterns. Print these photos at home or at a library. Try to make the photos the same size.

4  Cut the patterned objects out of the photos. Trace each one on construction paper. Cut out the shapes.

5  Recreate each pattern on its cutout. Think about the properties of each pattern. Then get creative! Maybe you want to use a brighter color in a leaf pattern or copy a pattern's stripes using different colors.

6  Glue each of your artworks to a sheet of construction paper. Then glue each one to a larger piece of construction paper to make frames.

7  Hang your pattern gallery on a wall!

# Emoji Sundial

Use math and sunshine to tell time in an ancient way with a modern artistic twist!

## Materials:

cardboard, scissors, paint, paintbrush, marker, box cutter, sharpened pencil, school glue, rock

1. Cut a large circle out of cardboard. Paint the circle. Let the paint dry.

2. Paint an emoji face on the circle. Write the number 12 in marker near the top edge of the emoji.

3. Have an adult use a box cutter to make a small slit in the center of the circle. Stick the sharp end of the pencil into the slit.

4. Tilt the pencil toward the number 12. Put glue on the slit to hold the pencil in place. Let the glue dry.

5. At noon on a sunny day, take your emoji sundial outside. Set it on a flat surface.

6. Arrange the sundial so the pencil's shadow rests over the 12. Set a rock on the sundial to keep it from moving in the wind.

7. Return to the sundial at 1:00. Write the number 1 near the edge of the sundial where the pencil's shadow lands.

8. Return to the sundial each hour until dusk. Add each hour's time to the sundial.

9. The sundial marks can change with the seasons. Reset your sundial each season by painting over the numbers and repeating steps 5 through 8.

## STEAM Takeaway

Before clocks were invented, people used sundials! These devices tell the time based on the sun's position in the sky, which changes throughout the day. Ancient Romans often marked their sundials with Roman numerals. Research Roman numerals. Try using them on your sundial.

# Wild Art Lab

Mix, mash, squeeze, and stamp natural materials to experiment with substances, texture, and tints!

## Materials:

gathered natural materials such as grasses, leaves, bark, moss, twigs, and flowers; pencil; notebook; plain paper; chenille stems; tempera paint; watercolor paint; water; ink pad

1. Get permission from an adult to explore outdoors. This could be in your yard, a park, or any natural area. Gather materials such as grasses, leaves, bark, moss, twigs, and flowers.

2. Examine the materials. How could they work as art tools? Moss and bark may make good stamps. Grasses and leaves could be used as paintbrushes.

3. Think about which materials could be mediums. Would leaves work like crayons when rubbed on paper? Would flowers? Could flower pollen work like paint or be sprinkled like glitter? Write your hypotheses in a notebook.

4. Try your hypotheses to see if they work. Tie grasses, leaves, or twigs together with chenille stems. Then paint and draw with them. Press moss or bark onto an ink pad and stamp them on the paper. Rub the paper with grasses, petals, or leaves.

5. Squeeze, rub, mix, and mash as many materials onto your paper as you like.

6. Compare the results to your hypotheses. Which materials worked best as art tools? Which made the best mediums? How did the materials interact with the paper?

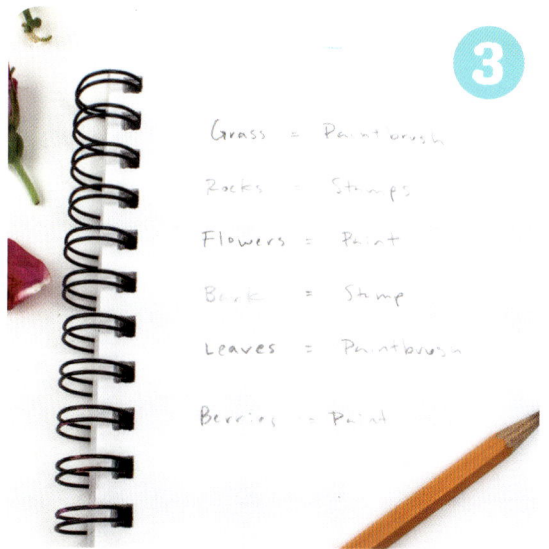

# Weather Vane

Learn about meteorology by making a working wind tool!

## Materials:

air-dry clay, 8 colored pencils, pencil with an eraser, chenille stems, paper straw, thumbtack

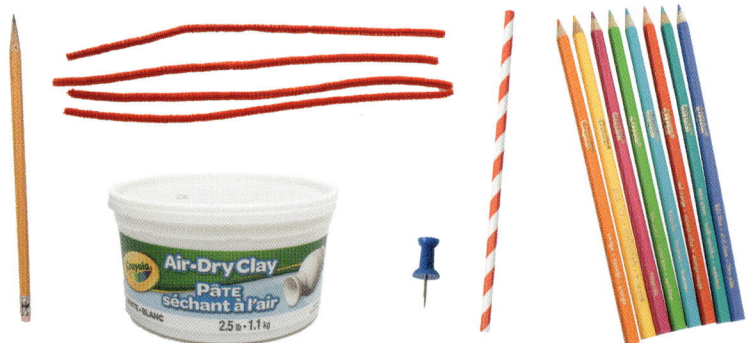

1 Form a large ball of clay. Flatten it into a thick disk. Push the colored pencils into the outer edge. Space them evenly. Push the pencil's point into the top of the disk. Make sure it is in the center of the disk. The pencil should be as vertical as possible. Let the clay dry.

2 Bend four chenille stems into the letters N, S, E, and W. These stand for *north*, *south*, *east*, and *west*. Use chenille stems to attach a letter to the end of every other colored pencil. Arrange the letters clockwise: N, E, S, W.

3 Wrap the end of a chenille stem around one end of the straw. Bend the chenille stem into an arrow shape. Wrap the end of another chenille stem around the other end of the straw. Bend the chenille stem into a tail fletching.

4 Set the straw on top of the vertical pencil. The pencil should be slightly closer to the arrow end. Have an adult help you push the thumbtack through the straw into the top of the pencil's eraser.

5 Set your weather vane outside on a level surface. Turn it so the N pencil points north.

6 Watch your vane spin in the wind! Whichever letter the arrow rests above is the direction the wind is blowing.

## STEAM Takeaway

Meteorologists study Earth's weather, climate, and atmosphere. They use weather vanes to help predict the weather. Knowing the direction of the wind can tell them when storms will arrive or when the temperature will change.

# Creeping Leaves Sequence

Design a vibrant vine via a mathematical pattern.

## Materials:

gathered leaves, card stock, pencil, scissors, construction paper, notebook, string; optional: markers, crayons, small hole punch

1. Get permission from an adult to gather three leaves. These could be from trees at a park or houseplants. The leaves should have different shapes.

2. Trace each leaf on card stock and cut out the shapes. Trace the cutouts between ten and twenty times each on construction paper. Use a different color for each type of leaf. Cut out the shapes.

3. Use markers or crayons to add details to the colored cutouts if you like.

4. Sort the cutouts by color. Each will represent one letter: A, B, or C. In a notebook, write down which color represents each letter.

5. Think of a sequence for the letters. This could be A, A, B, B, C, C. Another example is A, B, C, B, A. Write your sequence in the notebook.

6. Use a pencil point or hole punch to make a small hole near the edge of each leaf cutout.

7. Put the leaves on the string in the order of your sequence. Repeat the sequence until you run out of leaf cutouts. This will create a creeping vine.

8. Hang your sequence across your bedroom or another space.

## STEAM Takeaway

A sequence is a mathematical series of numbers or things in a repeating order. In nature, many plants and animals have shape or color sequences in their markings.

# Bug Jars

Build clay insects and bottle them among bits of their habitats.

## Materials:

digital camera, smartphone, or tablet; natural objects, such as twigs, leaves, grass, moss, and stones; printer; small bowl; water; air-dry clay; toothpicks; paint; paintbrushes; clear plastic jars with lids; scissors; school glue

1. Get permission from an adult to explore outdoors. This could be in your yard, a park, or any natural area. Look for insects in this area.

2. Don't catch the insects. Instead, take photos of them. Include the insects' habitats in the photos. If you don't see any insects, it's okay! Move on to step 3.

3. Gather twigs, leaves, grass, moss, stones, and other natural objects.

4. Print a few of your insect photos. If you didn't see any insects, find pictures of insects online.

5. Fill a small bowl with water. Use clay and toothpicks to create the insects. Use the water to keep the clay wet while you are working. Let the clay insects dry overnight.

6. Paint the insects. Let the paint dry.

7. Arrange the natural objects you gathered in the jars. If the twigs are long, have an adult help you cut or break them until the twigs fit inside the jars.

8. Glue each insect to a twig. Let the glue dry. Place the twigs inside the jars. Then put your bug jars on display!

# Rain Forest in a Box

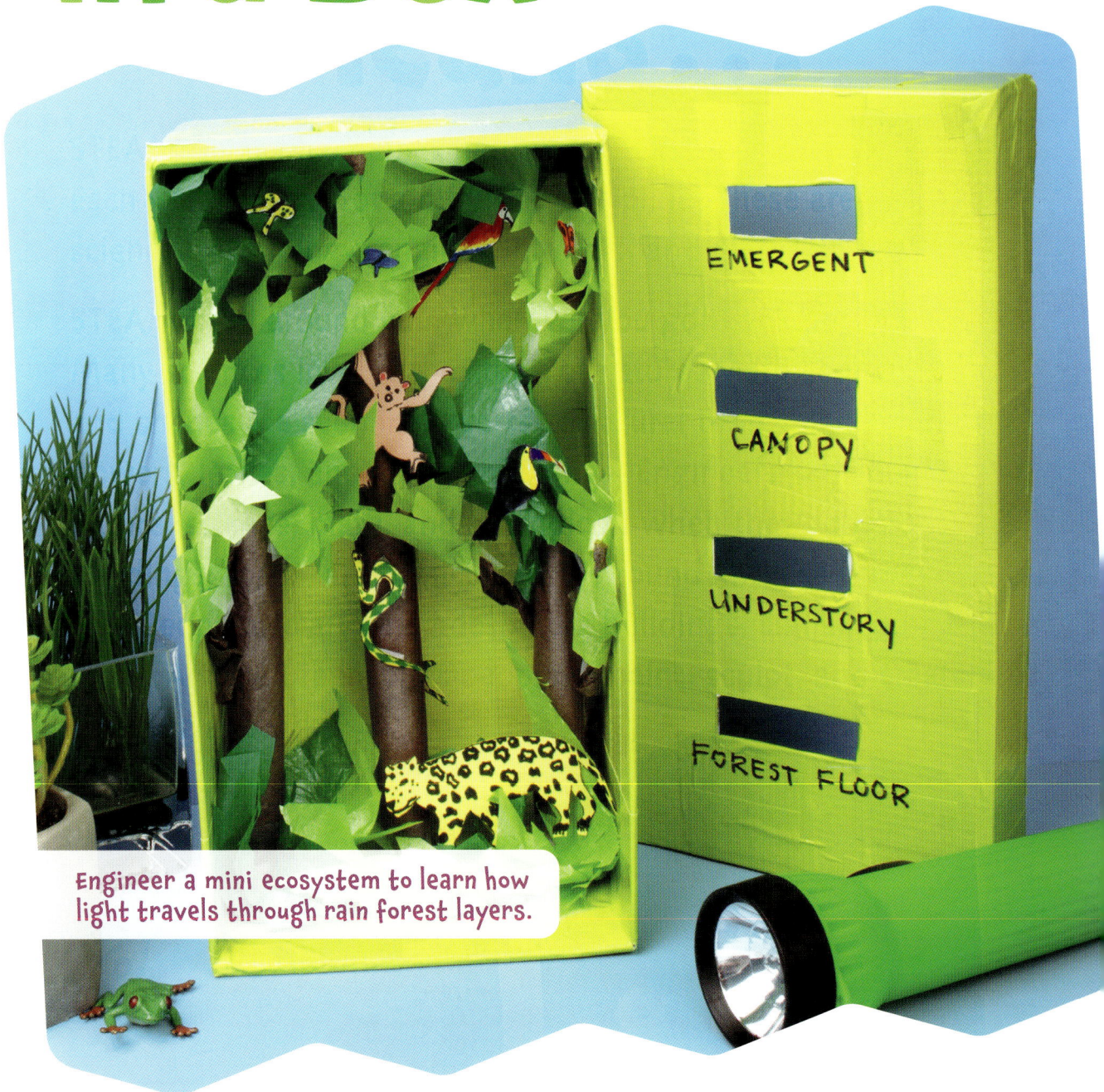

Engineer a mini ecosystem to learn how light travels through rain forest layers.

EMERGENT

CANOPY

UNDERSTORY

FOREST FLOOR

## Materials:

tablet or computer, pencil, notebook, shoebox, scissors, green duct tape, construction paper, tape, brown and green tissue paper, school glue, markers, crayons, flashlight

**1** Research rain forest layers online. Write down the layer names in a notebook. Include some animals that live in each layer.

**2** Draw four lines across the inside of the shoebox lid. Space the lines evenly. Draw a small rectangle under each line. Have an adult cut out the rectangles as well as one rectangle on a short side of the shoebox.

**3** Cover the box and lid with green duct tape.

**4** Label each hole in the lid with a rain forest layer. Make sure the layers are in the correct order from top to bottom.

Project continued on next page.

5 Tightly roll a sheet of brown construction paper into a tube. Tape the edge. Place lines of glue on brown tissue paper. Roll the tube up in the tissue paper. Trim any extra tissue paper.

6 Cut the tube from step 5 to make it slightly shorter than the length of the box. This will be a tree trunk.

7 Repeat steps 5 and 6 to make several more tree trunks.

8 Cut squares of brown tissue paper and twist them into branches. Tape them to the tree trunks.

**9** Cut leaf shapes out of green tissue paper. Tape some leaves to the branches. Set the box so the hole is at the top. Tape the trees inside the box.

**10** Tape leftover leaves to the bottom of the box. These are shrubs and plants.

**11** Draw animals from each rain forest layer on construction paper. Cut the animals out. Tape them to the trees or to the bottom of the box. Make sure they are in the correct layers.

**12** Put the lid on the box and stand it upright. Shine a flashlight through the top hole. Look through the holes in the lid. The flashlight acts like the sun shining down on the rain forest. How much light reaches the forest floor?

# Symmetrical Stick Mandala

Paint, wrap, and weave a pattern to create cool, colorful wall art.

## Materials:

tablet or computer, notebook or paper, pencil, several small sticks of roughly the same size, paint, paintbrushes, air-dry clay, chenille stems, yarn, colored pencils

1  Research mandalas online. Study their symmetry.

2  Sketch a design for a simple, symmetrical mandala base. The base will look like a snowflake.

3  Get permission from an adult to explore outdoors. This could be in your yard, a park, or any natural area. Bring your drawing and search for small sticks to match your design.

4  Arrange your gathered sticks on your base design. If some are too long, have an adult help you cut or break them.

5  Paint the sticks. Let the paint dry.

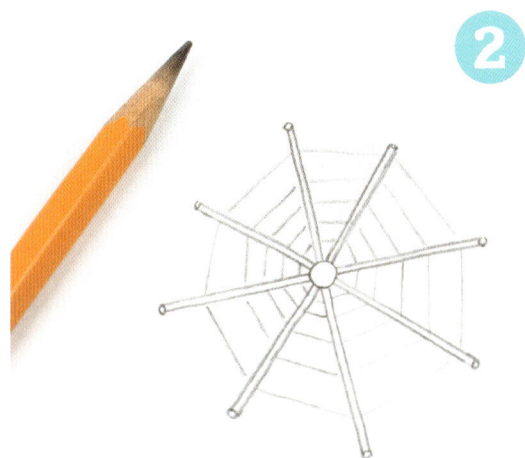

Project continued on next page.

**6** Form a large ball of clay. Flatten it into a thick disk. Push the ends of the sticks into the outer edge to create your mandala base design. Let the clay dry overnight.

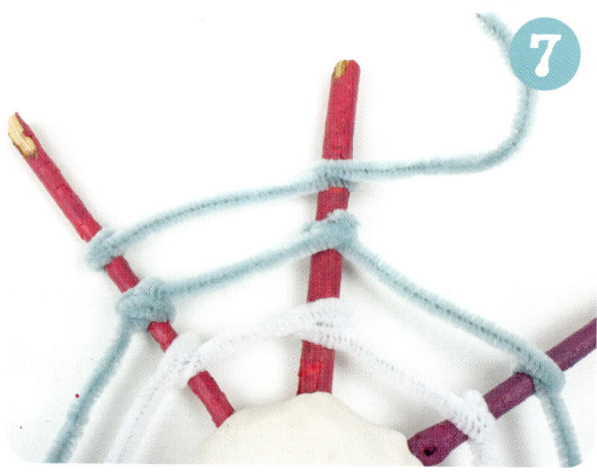

**7** Wrap chenille stems around and across the sticks to form rows across the sections. Count to make sure each section has the same number of rows. Make sure the rows are all about the same distance apart.

**8** Choose yarn colors. Decide how many rows of each color to weave in each section to create a symmetrical pattern. Draw your pattern on the sketch of the mandala. This will help you keep track while you are weaving.

**9** Cut a long length of yarn. Tie one end to the chenille stem closest to the clay.

**10** Weave the yarn through the rows of chenille stems to the outside edge of the mandala. To create a second row of the same color, simply weave the yarn back toward the center.

**11** Keep weaving back and forth until you reach the end of the yarn or want to change colors. Tie the yarn to the nearest chenille stem. Cut off any extra yarn.

**12** Repeat steps 9 through 11 to complete the pattern in all sections of your mandala.

**13** Tie a loop of yarn to the mandala. Use it to hang your mandala masterpiece somewhere special!

## STEAM
### Takeaway

Mandalas are geometric designs used in meditation and in some religions. Mandalas usually have circular, symmetrical patterns. These types of patterns are also found in flowers, snowflakes, and much more.

# MAKER REMIX!
# Creeping Leaves Sequence

The Creeping Leaves Sequence project on page 16 explores creating a vine using sequences of leaves. How could you change or expand the activity? Here are some ideas:

- Add two new colors and shapes of leaves. Label them D and E. Write a new sequence using A, B, C, D, and E. Then create a vine using the new sequence.

- Make several shorter strings using different sequences. Tie them to a stick next to each other to make a wall decoration.

- Cut the leaf shapes out of card stock or thin cardboard. These are sturdier than paper. Use these leaves to build a 3D structure. Have an adult cut slits in the leaves. Use the slits to fit the leaves together. How could this 3D structure display sequence too?

How does having rows of the leaves next to one another affect their sequence patterns? Look for patterns vertically on your leaf collage or 3D tower. Now look for patterns horizontally and even diagonally!

# GLOSSARY

**diagonally:** positioned or moving in a manner that is not straight across or up and down

**discipline:** an area of study

**engineering:** the science of designing and building complicated products, machines, systems, or structures

**fletching:** the feathers on an arrow

**geometric:** made up of points, lines, and angles

**habitats:** the places where plants and animals grow or live in nature

**horizontally:** positioned or moving in a manner that is side to side rather than up and down

**hypotheses:** ideas or theories that need to be studied or tested to be proven

**mediums:** materials or methods used by artists

**meteorology:** the science that deals with the atmosphere, weather, and weather forecasting

**predict:** to say that something will or might happen in the future

**symmetrical:** having two sides or halves that are the same in size, shape, color, and position

**texture:** the way something feels when you touch it

**3D:** having width, depth, and height

**vertical:** positioned or moving up and down rather than side to side

**weather vane:** a movable device that shows which way the wind is blowing

# LEARN MORE

Crayola: Create It Yourself—Rock Art Animals
https://www.crayola.com/crafts/rock-art-animals-craft/

Dickmann, Nancy. *Math in Nature*. Minneapolis: Hungry Tomato, 2019.

The Kid Should See This—How Does Michael Grab Make Impossible Rock Structures?
https://thekidshouldseethis.com/post/michael-grab-balancing-rocks

Kington, Emily. *Make a Nature Sculpture*. Minneapolis: Hungry Tomato, 2020.

Science Kids—Nature for Kids
https://www.sciencekids.co.nz/nature.html

Weather Wiz Kids
http://www.weatherwizkids.com/

Yi, Andrea Scalzo. *100 Easy STEAM Activities: Awesome Hands-On Projects for Aspiring Artists and Engineers*. Salem, MA: Page Street Publishing Co., 2019.

# INDEX

# PHOTO ACKNOWLEDGMENTS

The images in this book are used with the permission of: © Amelia Fox/ Shutterstock Images, p. 4 (girl w/flower); © Morrowind/Shutterstock Images, p. 4 (STEM symbols); © TinnaPong/Shutterstock Images, p. 5 (boys in forest); Veronica Thompson, pp. 10 (sundial), 11 (step 3), 11 (step 7). All other images are © Mighty Media, Inc.

Cover Photos: © Mighty Media, Inc.